Sparkly Christmas
Sticker Book

Illustrated by James Newman Gray

Designed by Emily Beevers
Words by Fiona Patchett

You'll find all the stickers at
the back of the book.

In the mountains

High in the mountains, animals whiz and whoosh down the glistening slopes. Add more animals on sleds, skis and snowboards.

Magical trees

Soft snowflakes fill the sky and settle on the trees, making them look magical in the twinkling lights. Help the animals add more shiny decorations.

Fairy helpers

Fairies flutter their wings to
reach the highest branches of the tree.
Some hang shimmering decorations,
while others play Christmassy songs.

Christmas snowmen

Snowmen sparkle white in the sunshine.
Help the animals give them scarves, gloves
and hats ready for Christmas.

On the ice

This dazzling frozen lake is the perfect place to ice skate. Add more penguins to glide and dance around the ice.

Santa's sleigh

Just a few more gifts to load onto his gleaming sleigh and Santa will be ready to soar through the night sky. Can you add some gifts and more elves to help him?

Snowy market

Twinkling lights make the snow-covered market stalls glitter and glow. Fill the scene with busy shoppers.

A market stall

There is so much to choose from at Squirrel's market stall. Help her fill her shelves with more gingerbread, candy and sparkly decorations.

Pages 2-3

Pages 4-5

Pages 6-7

Pages 8-9

Pages 10–11

Pages 12–13

Pages 2-3

Pages 4-5

Pages 6-7

Pages 8-9

Pages 10–11

Pages 12–13

Pages 14-15

Page 16